Sea Life

COLOR BY NUMBER
COLORING BOOK

George Toufexis

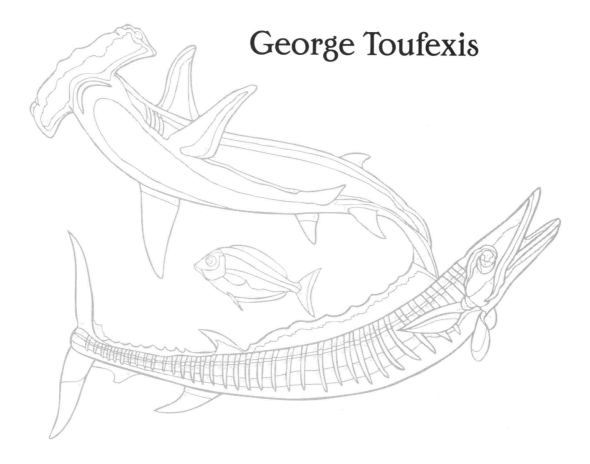

DOVER PUBLICATIONS, INC.
MINEOLA, NEW YORK

Bibliographical Note

Sea Life Color by Number Coloring Book, first published by Dover Publications, Inc.,
in 2015, is a revised edition of the work originally published by Dover in 2015.

This 2015 edition printed for Barnes & Noble, Inc., by Dover Publications, Inc.

International Standard Book Number
ISBN-13: 978-0-486-80384-5
ISBN-10: 0-486-80384-8

Manufactured in the United States by Courier Corporation

This coloring collection features beautiful underwater scenes in full-page designs for you to color. Each plate is shown in full-color on the inside covers. You can duplicate these images simply by following the color guide found on the inside front cover, or choose your own colors for a more personal touch. As part of Dover's *Creative Haven* series for the experienced colorist, each plate is highly detailed, and enclosed in a border for a finished look. Plus, the perforated, unbacked pages offer you the opportunity to experiment with any media you like, and make displaying your work easy!

The artwork in this book is based on 23 colors (black is used twice) that approximate a standard set of colored pencils. You can use more colors if you wish but the colors listed here will allow you to fully color the artwork.

Color number 1 is called "black shadow." It is the same as black, but is used to darken the color above, below, or next to it by "overlaying," which is a technique of lightly applying black over an existing color, or applying color over light black. You will notice that the "1" is usually very close to the color number it's supposed to darken. It's best to use a light touch when shading with black.

White is represented as a blank space with the exception of spaces that are too small or thin to house a number. In those cases, following the immediate color pattern will yield the best results.

TIPS AND TECHNIQUES

Because of the level of detail in this book, it is best to use hard colored pencils, allowing for a thinner line.

A good way to start is by moderately applying the lightest and darkest colors first. As you add the mid-range colors you will be able judge how intense the lights and darks need to be. (You can go over your colors several times.)

Although the color spaces have outlines separating them, it is better to let the colors "bleed" into each other for a softer appearance. This applies to fish, and especially to the background water colors. Exceptions are rocks and most outside edges.

You will also notice that there are various line thicknesses in the artwork. A good way to make your artwork "pop" is to go over some of the heavier gray outlines with black or a dark color. Remember that the further away an object is, the lighter the outline should be.

Finally, remember to turn your artwork so that your hand can comfortably move in the appropriate direction for the types of strokes you are using.

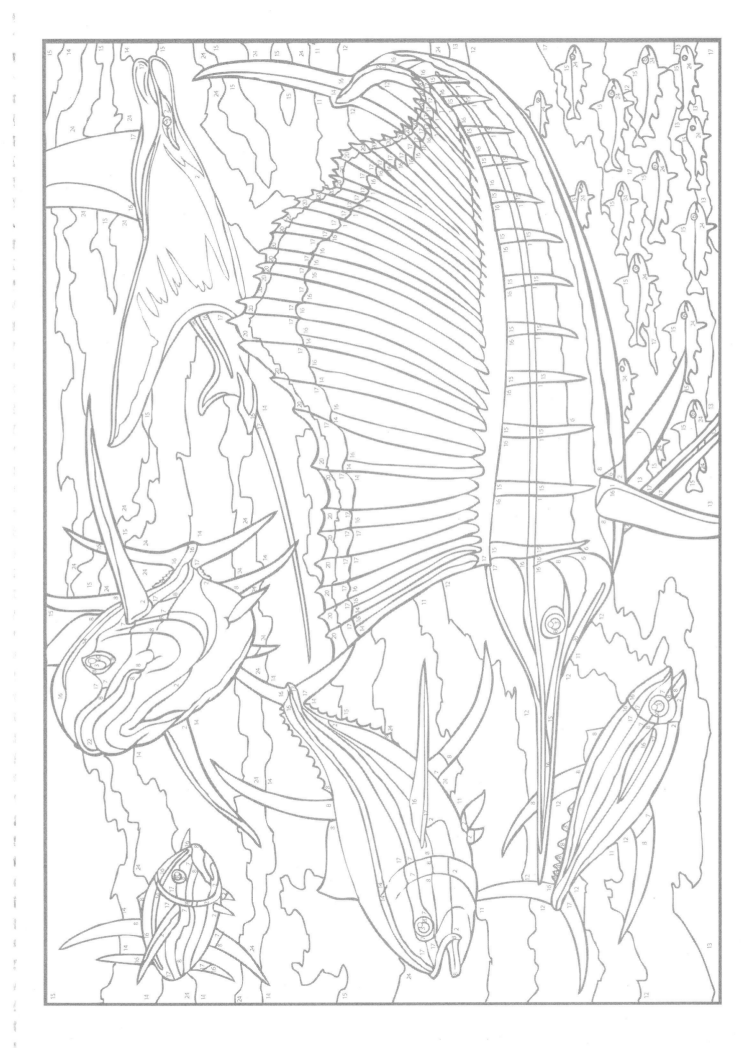

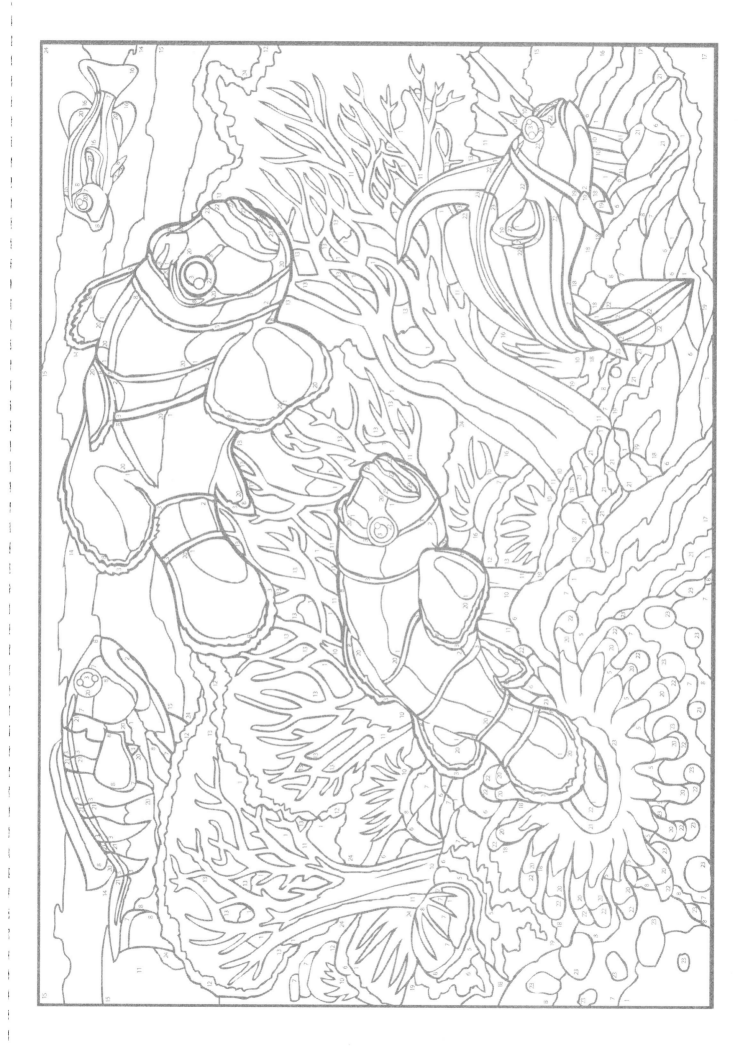

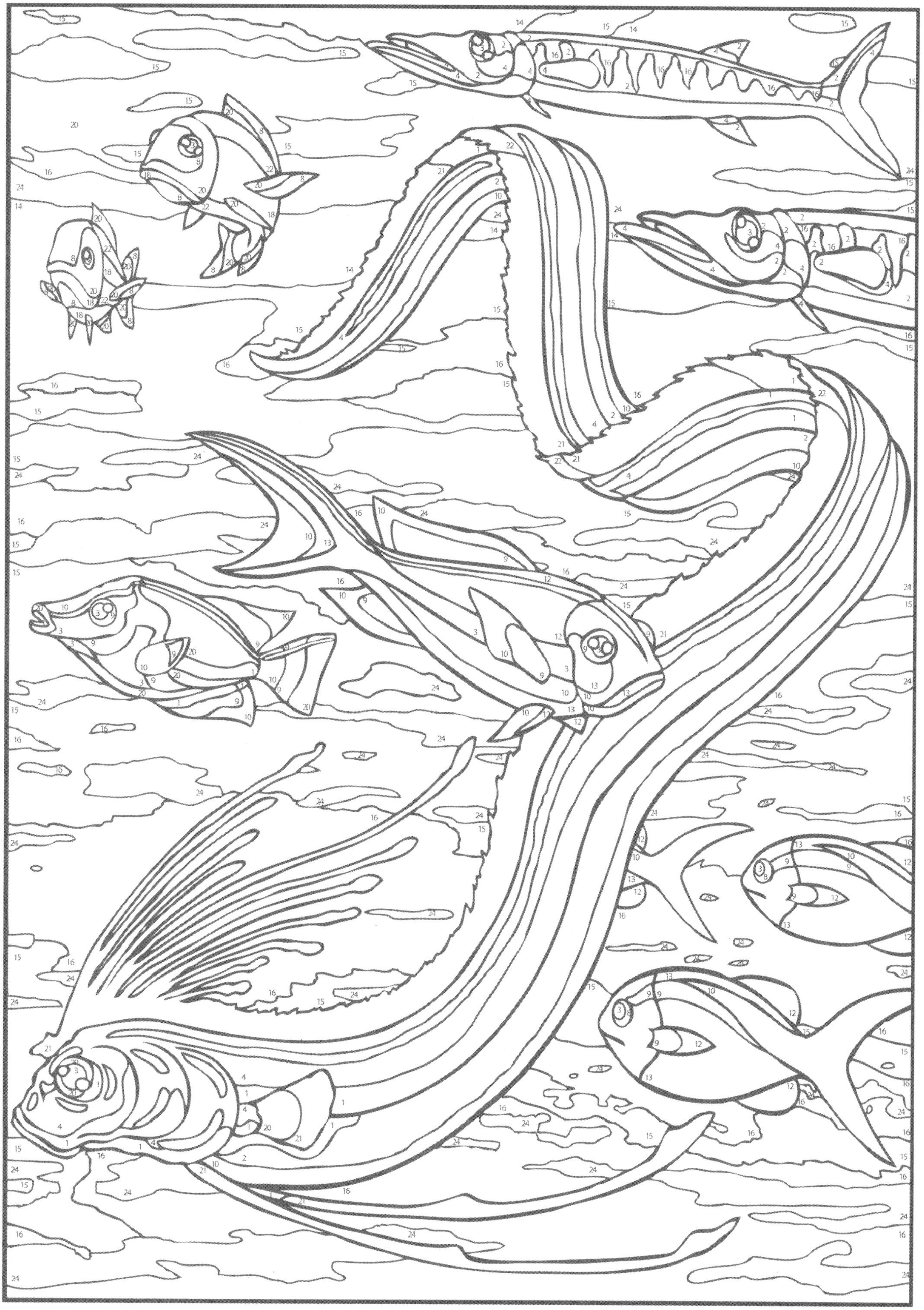